CONTENTS

BURN

Words and Music by NORAH JONES
and SARAH ODA

Moody groove

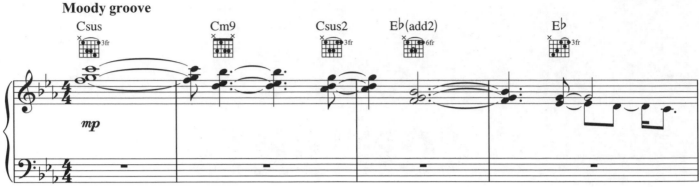

The plot be-gins___ with you___

___ and me in dark - lit rooms.___

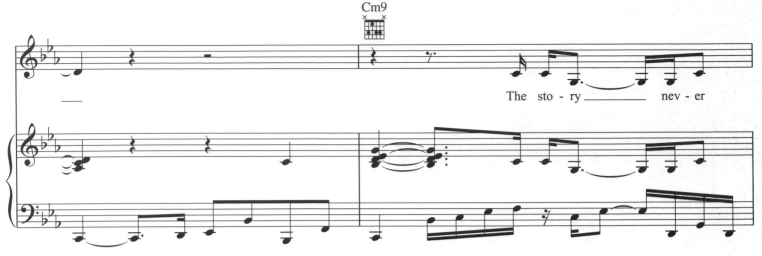

The sto - ry _____ nev - er

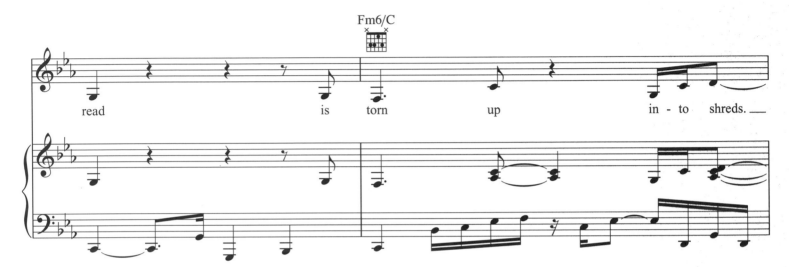

read _____ is torn up in - to shreds. _____

_____ I see it in _____ your eyes, _

the in - vi - ta - tion lies. _ The nev - er

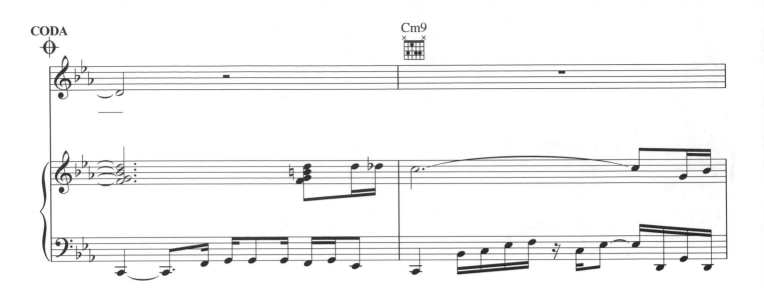

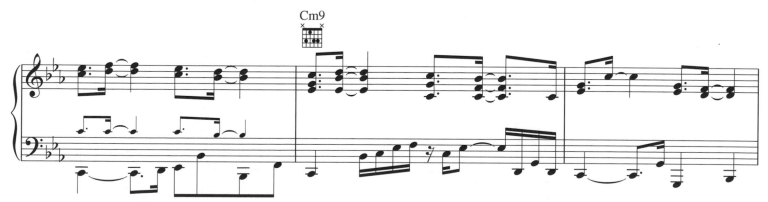

*Optional L.H. piano part

TRAGEDY

Words and Music by NORAH JONES
and SARAH ODA

Laid-Back Groove

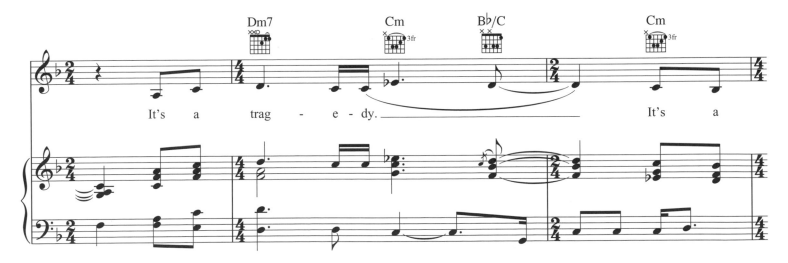

trag - e - dy. __ It's a trag - e - dy. __

__

He was on - ly twen - ty - five, __
Now he's fi - n'lly come a - round, __

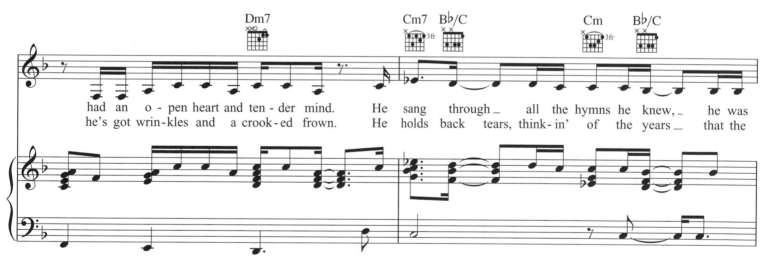

had an o - pen heart and ten - der mind. He sang through __ all the hymns he knew, __ he was
he's got wrin - kles and a crook - ed frown. He holds back tears, think - in' of the years __ that the

search - in' for a high - er sign. When his wa - ter was turned __ to wine, __
bot - tle had a long time down. So he'd sit, have an - oth - er round, __

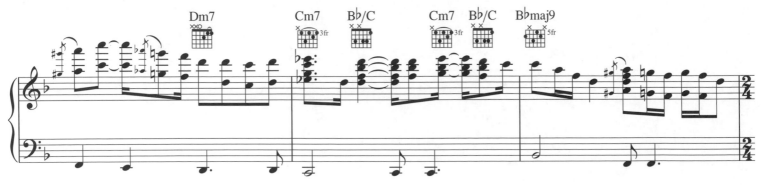

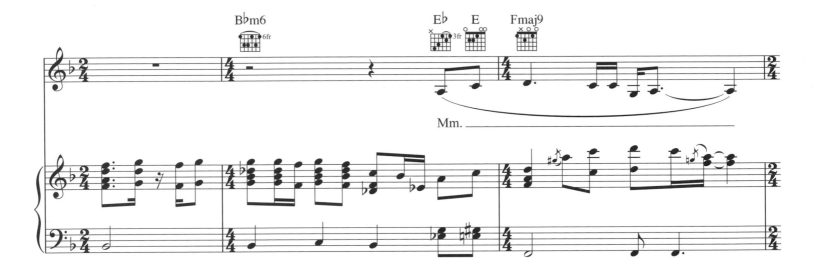

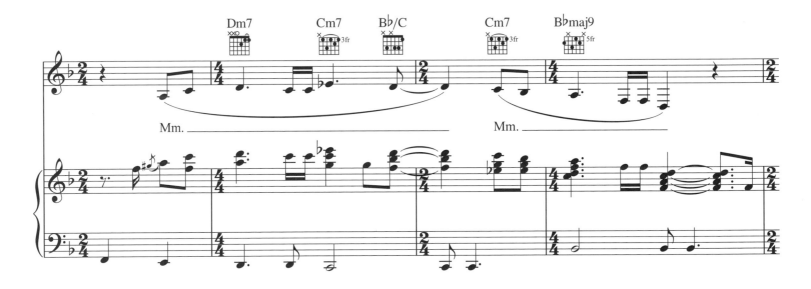

FLIPSIDE

Words and Music by NORAH JONES
and PETER REMM

Blues Rock

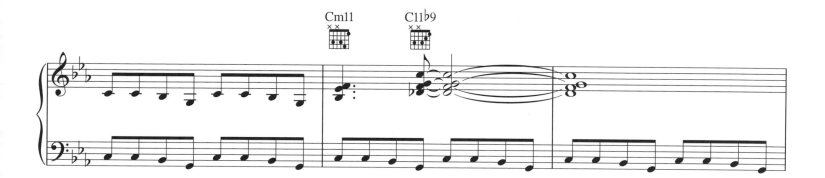

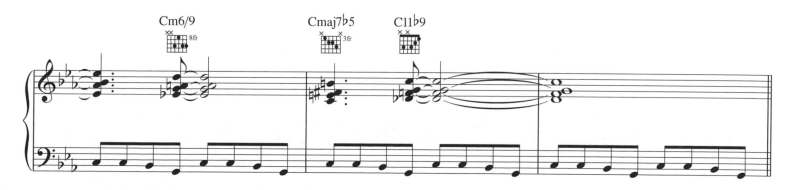

fin - al - ly know_ who I'm sup - posed to be,_ my mind was locked, but I_
saw_ your re - flec - tion_ all o - ver the news,_ your temp-'ra-ture's well_ past a

_ found the key. _ Hope it don't all slip a - way from me. _
hun-dred and two. _ Put the guns a - way_ or we're all_ gon - na lose. _

Hard times, _
Stand by _

fun lines. _
or take flight. _

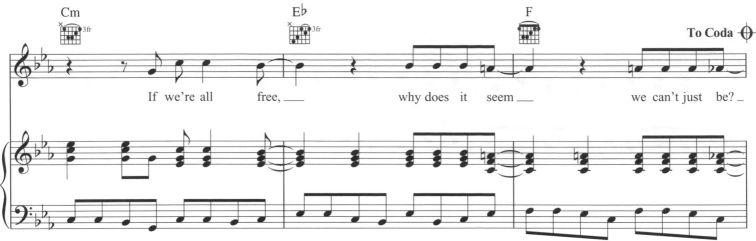

If we're all free, ____ why does it seem ___ we can't just be? __

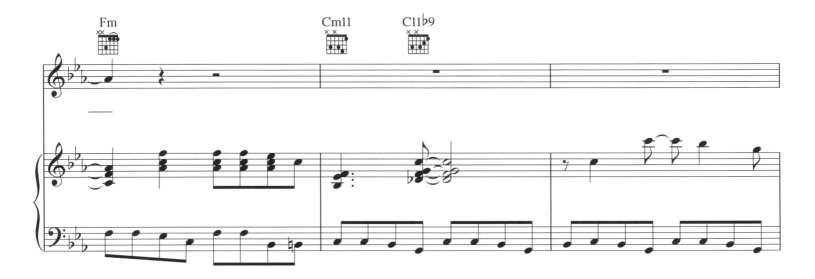

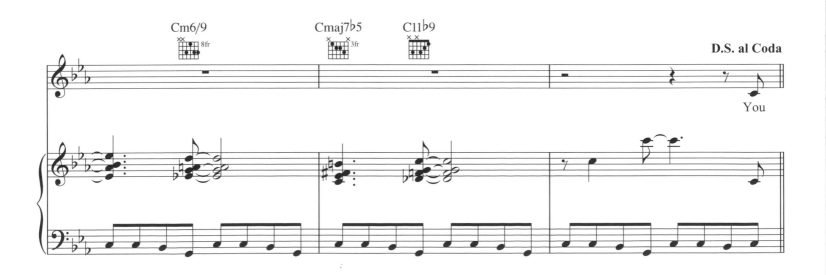

You

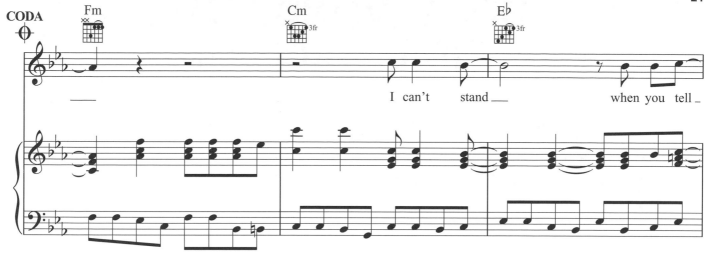

IT'S A WONDERFUL TIME FOR LOVE

Words and Music by NORAH JONES
and SARAH ODA

Fm7 *(implied)*

It's a won-der-ful time ___ for love. ___
won-der-ful time ___ for love. ___

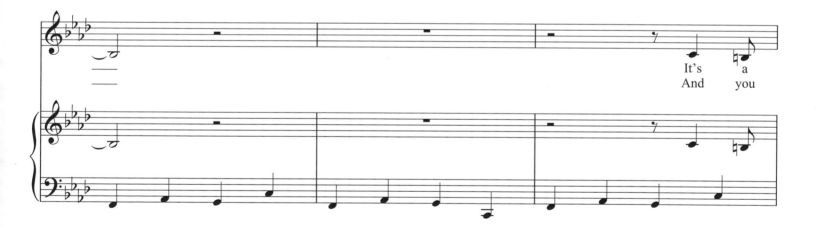

It's a
And you

won-der-ful time ___ for love. ___
think you have all ___ you dreamed of.

But

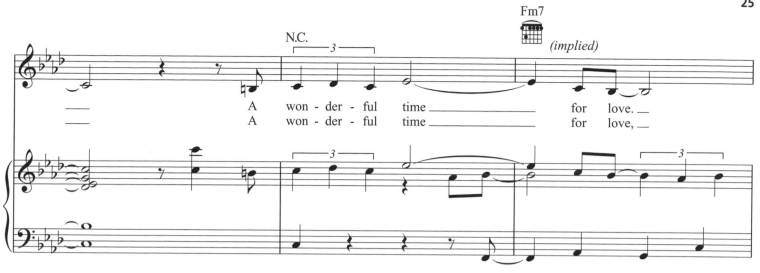

A won-der-ful time _____ for love. ___
A won-der-ful time _____ for love, ___

Time for deal - ing _____ a dif -
such a beau - ti - ful time

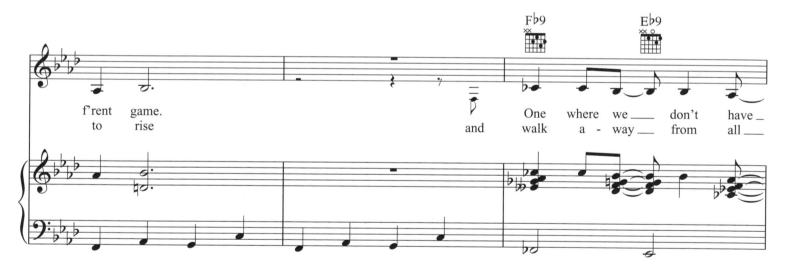

f'rent game.
to rise

and One where we ___ don't have ___
walk a - way ___ from all ___

to place the blame. ___
the end - less lies. ___

To Coda ⊕

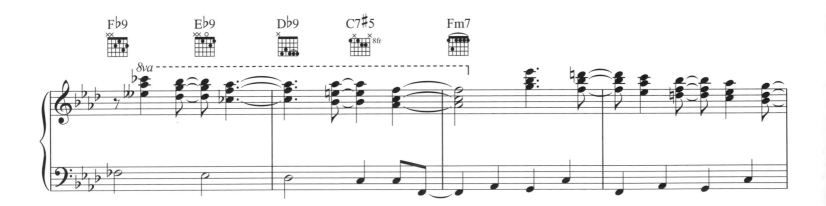

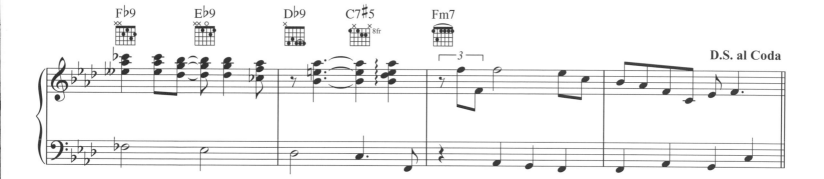

D.S. al Coda

CODA

And try to see the world through oth- er eyes. ___

Mmm. _____

DAY BREAKS

Words and Music by NORAH JONES
and PETER REMM

Mellow groove

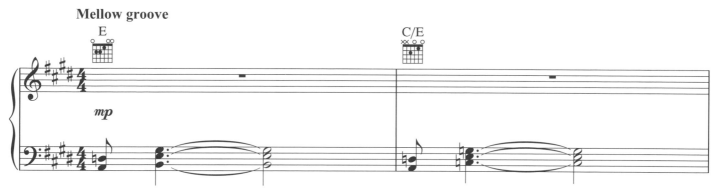

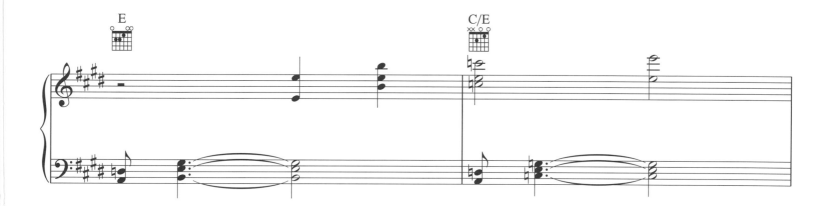

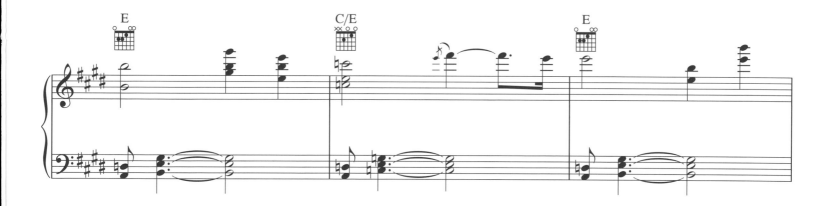

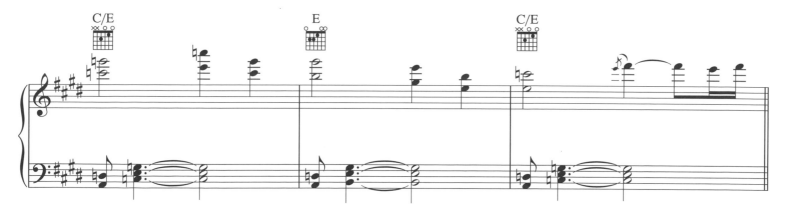

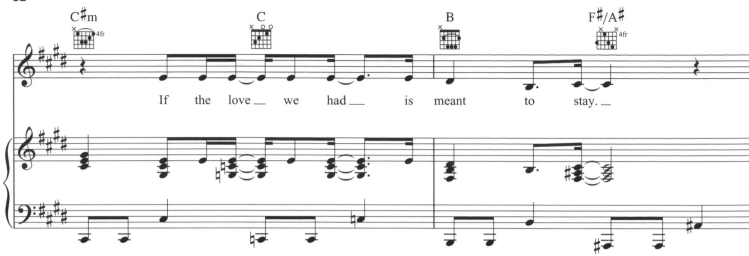

If the love __ we had __ is meant to stay. __

Find a place __ to call __ your own.

No need to roam __ a - round __ the rooms that once made

D.S. al Coda

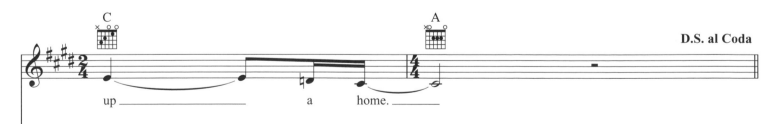

up _____ a home. ___

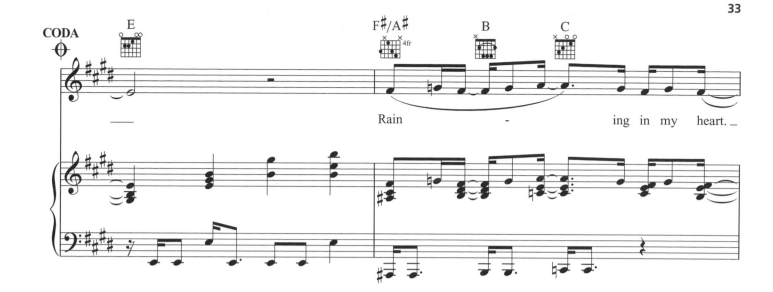

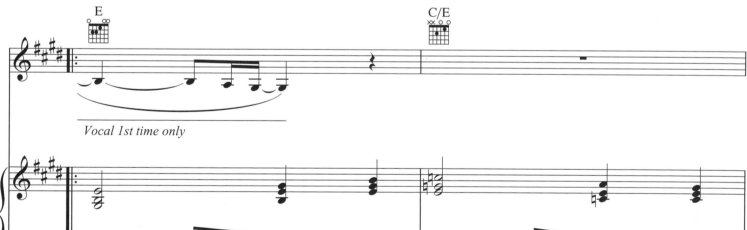

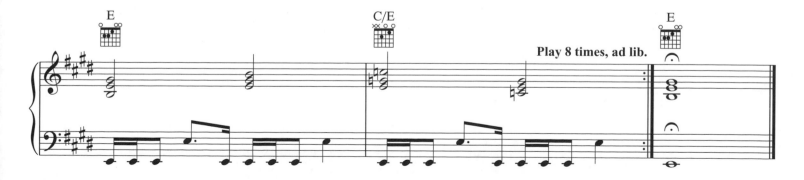

AND THEN THERE WAS YOU

Words and Music by NORAH JONES
and PETER REMM

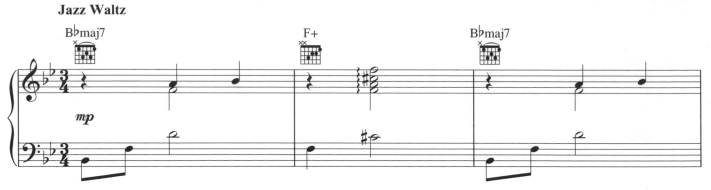

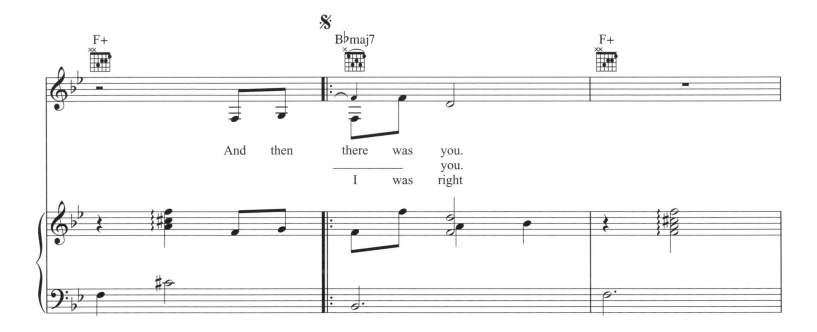

And then there was you.
_____ you.
I was right

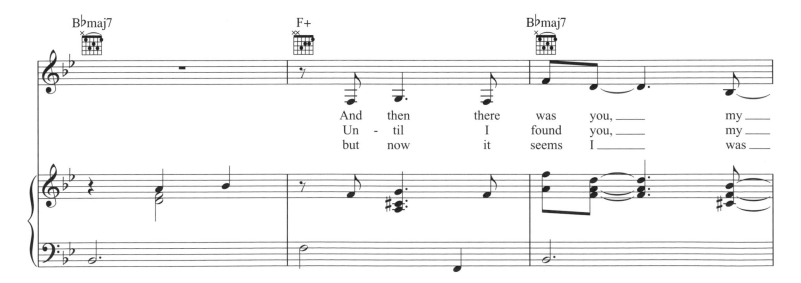

And then there was you, _____ my _____
Un - til I found you, _____ my _____
but now it seems I _____ was _____

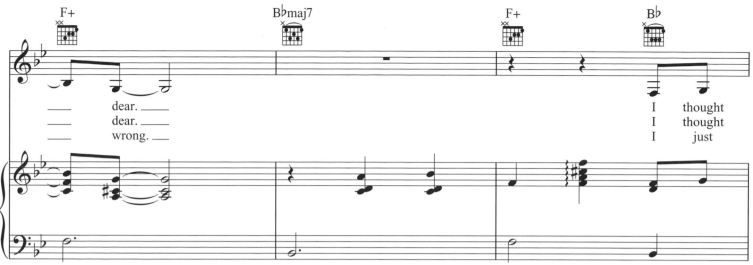

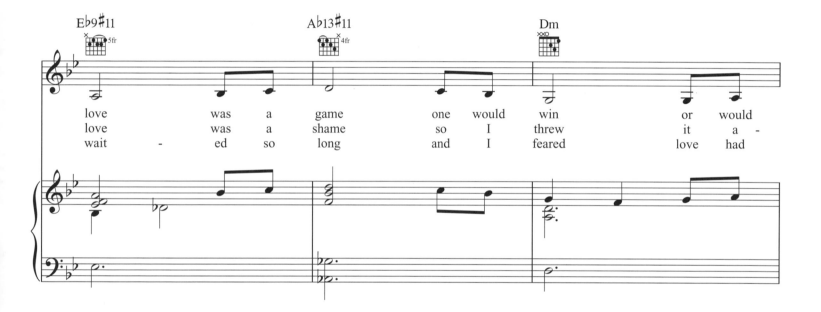

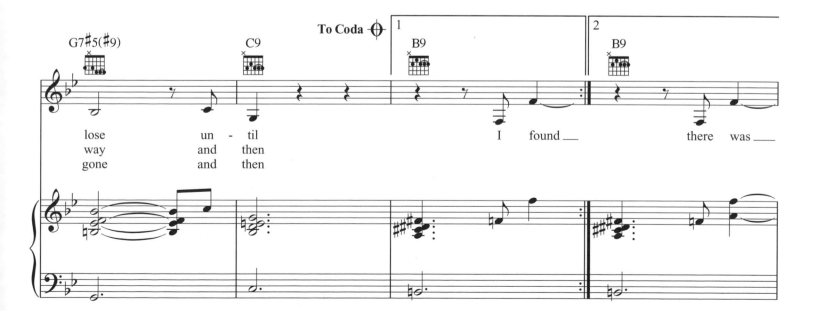

you.

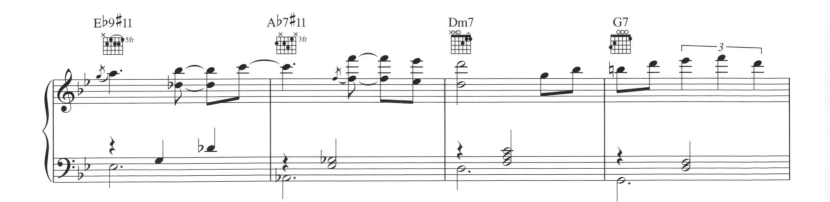

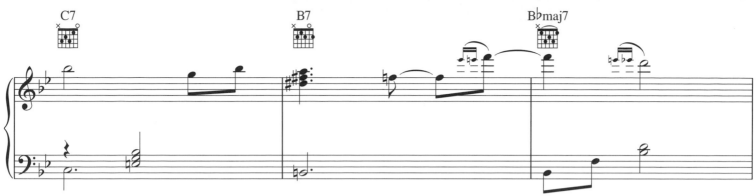

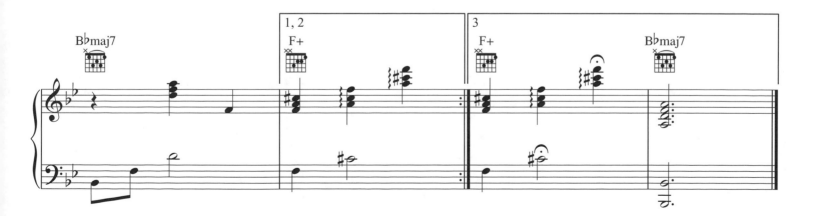

DON'T BE DENIED

Words and Music by
NEIL YOUNG

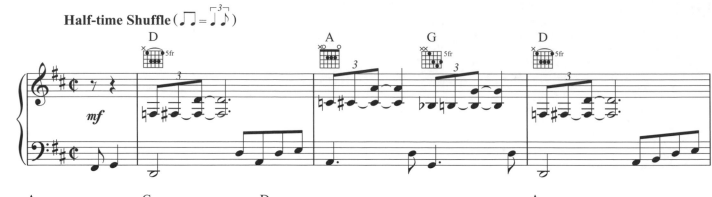

They packed up all _____ their bags _____ and drove up to
The punch - es came fast and hard, _____ ly - in' on her

An - chor - age. _____
back in the school yard. _____

Oh, _____

don't be _____ de - nied, _____ don't be _____ de - nied,

don't be de - nied,_____

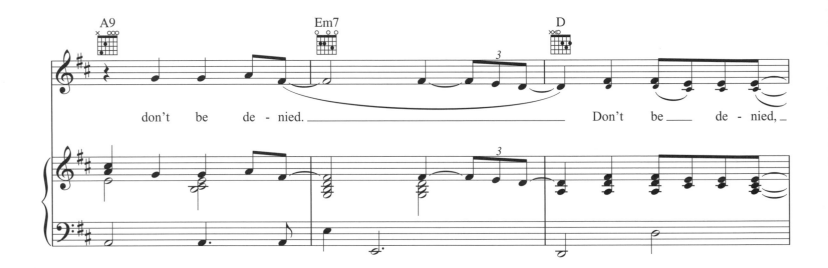

don't be de - nied._____ Don't be ___ de - nied, _

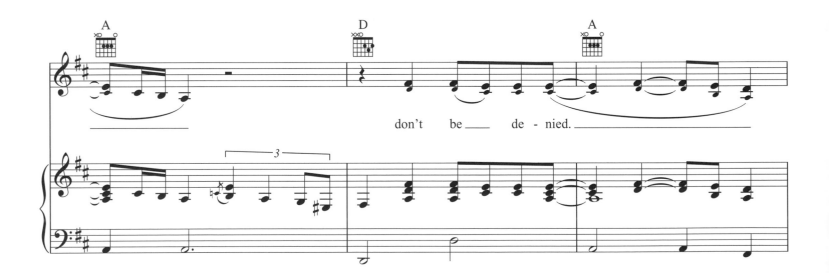

don't be ___ de - nied._____

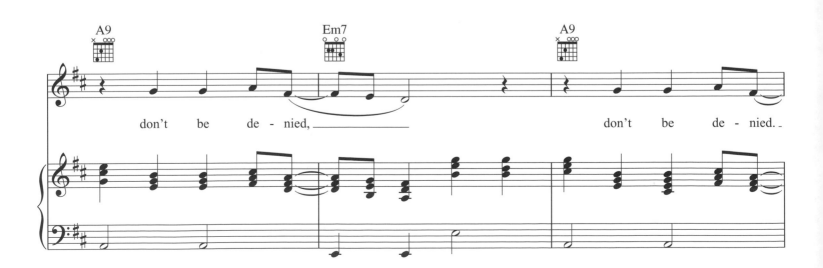

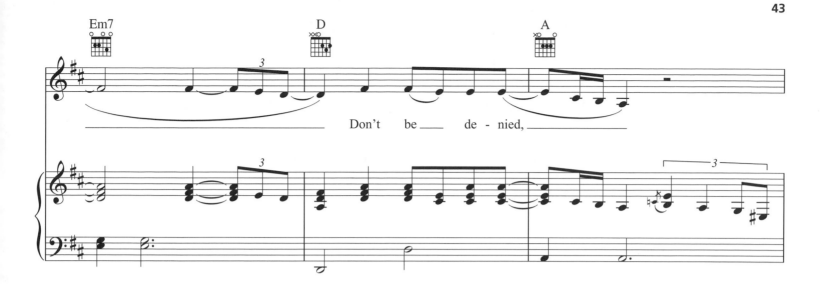

Don't be ___ de - nied, ___

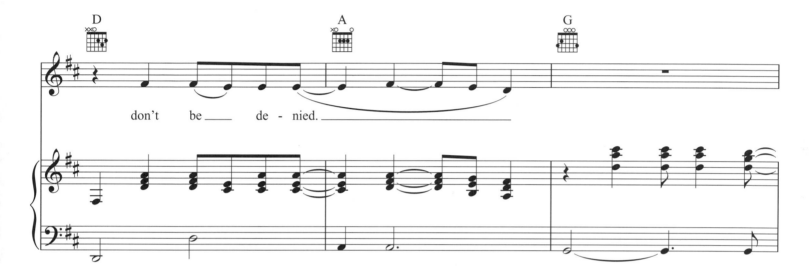

don't be ___ de - nied. ___

Organ solo ad lib.

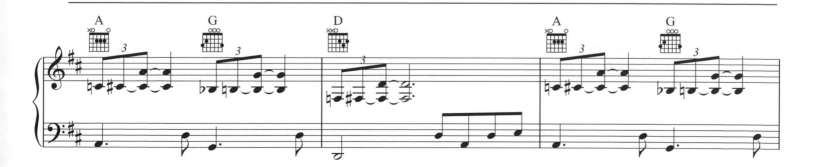

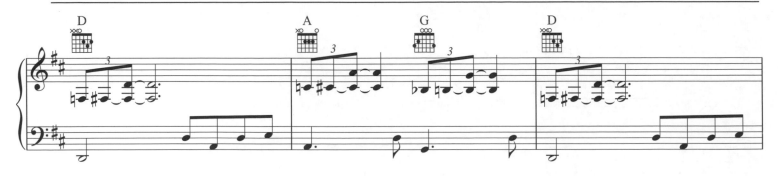

D.S. al Coda

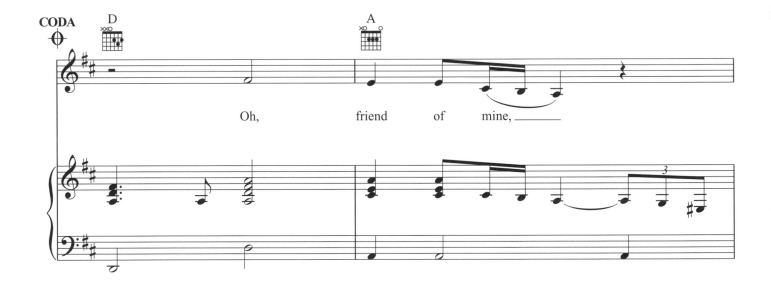

Oh, friend of mine, _____

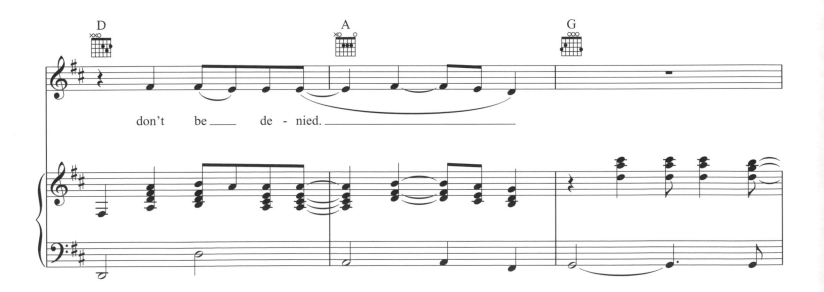

don't be ___ de - nied. _____

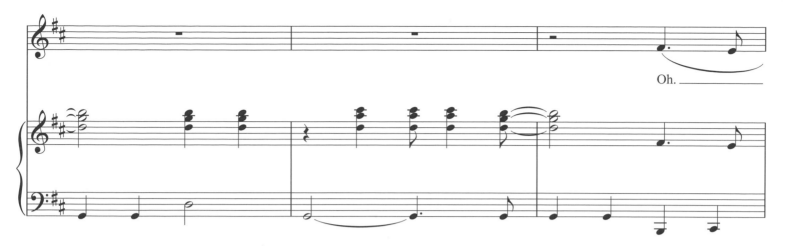

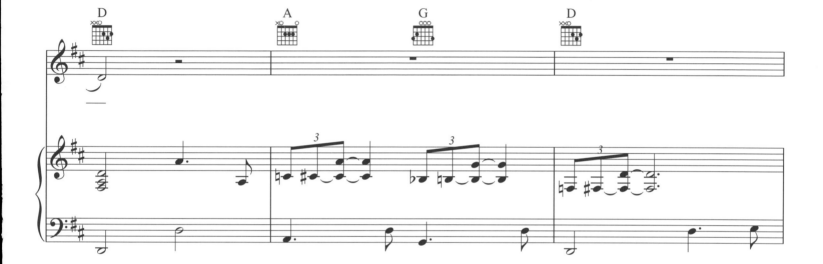

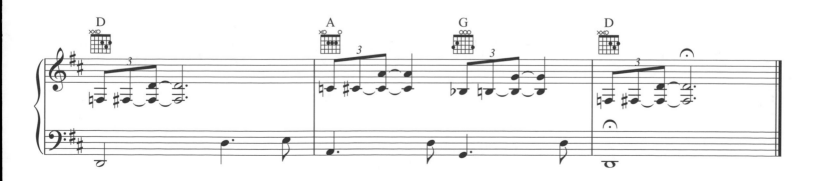

PEACE

Words and Music by
HORACE SILVER

Grooving Ballad

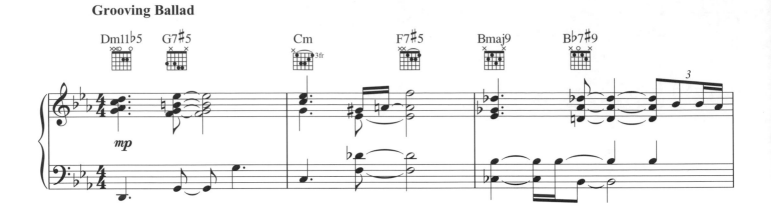

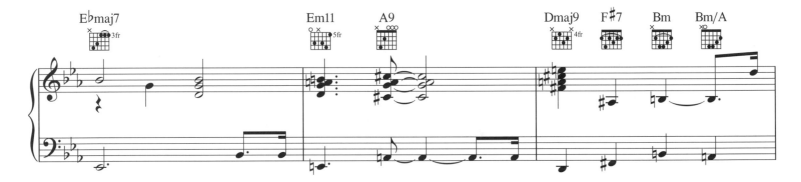

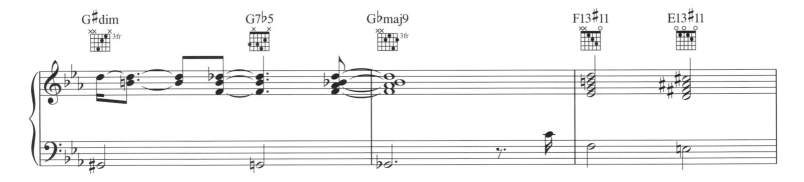

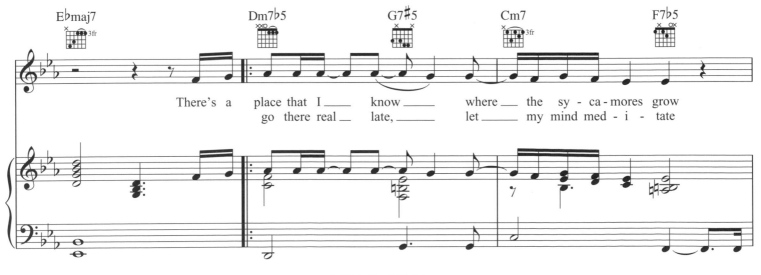

There's a place that I ___ know ___ where ___ the sy - ca - mores grow
go there real ___ late, ___ let ___ my mind med - i - tate

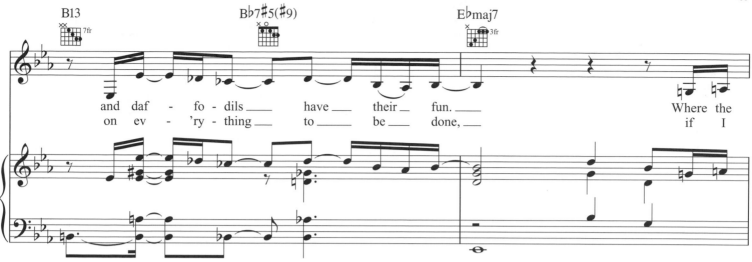

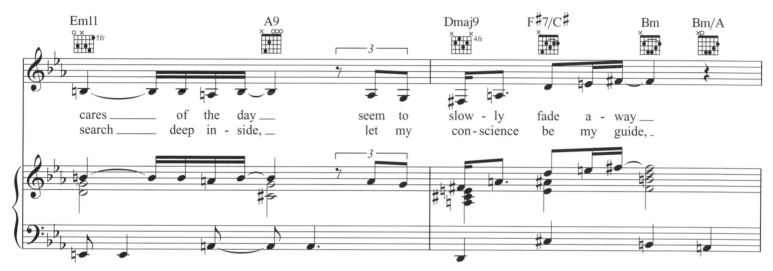

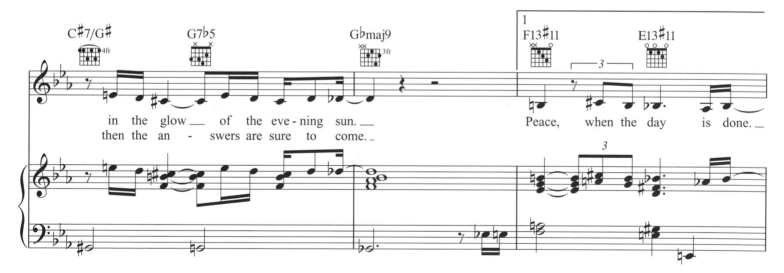

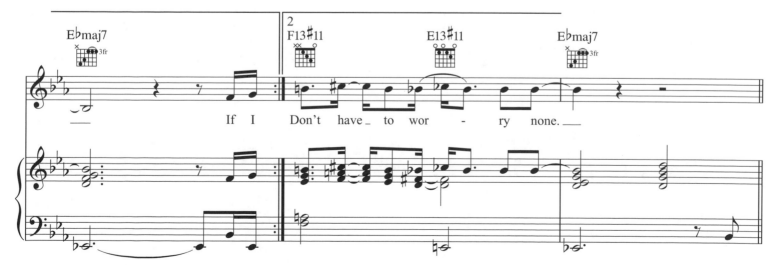

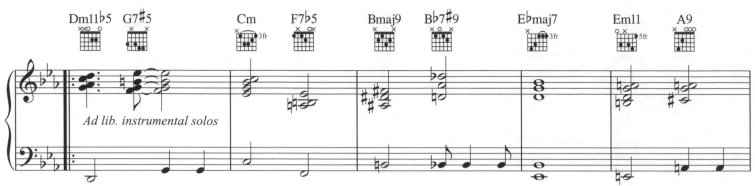

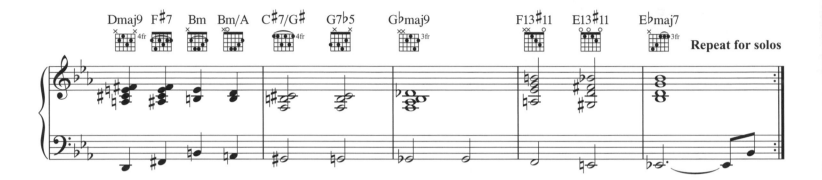

mean-ing comes _ to you, _ and the free-dom _ you seek _ is won. _

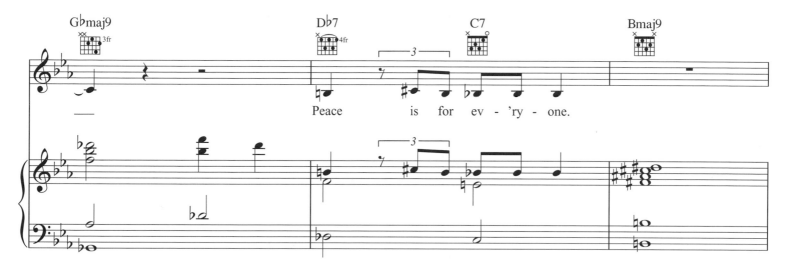

_ Peace is for ev-'ry - one.

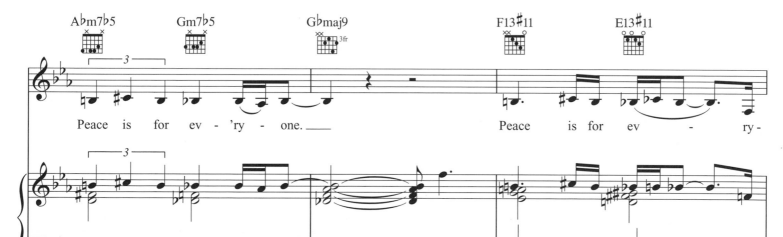

Peace is for ev-'ry - one. _ Peace is for ev - ry -

one.

SLEEPING WILD

Words and Music by
SARAH ODA

Mellow Swing

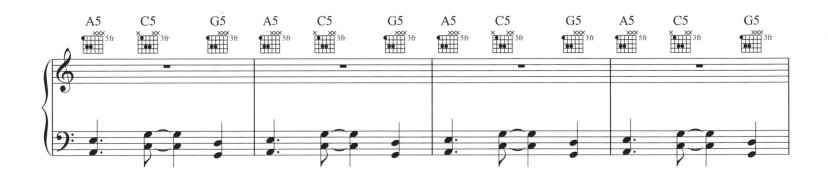

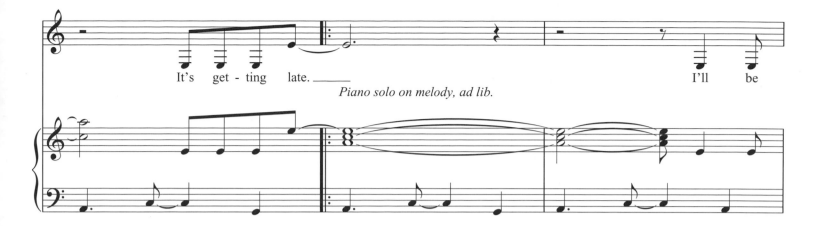

It's get - ting late. _____

Piano solo on melody, ad lib.

I'll be

Bdim

E7/B

on my way. _ Seems that you have noth - ing left to say. _

Am

But ___ now that you

Bdim

E7/B

have had ___ a few, words that were lost ___ have _

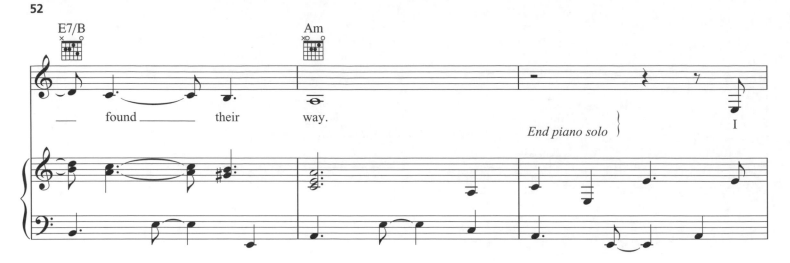

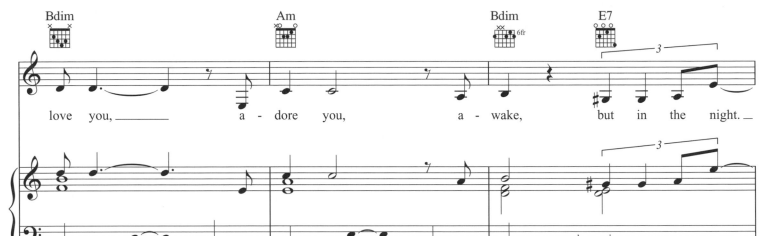

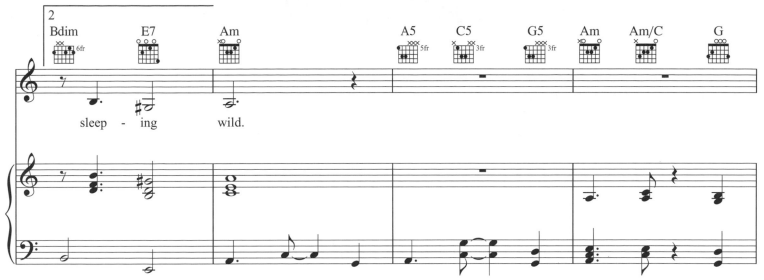

sleep - ing wild.

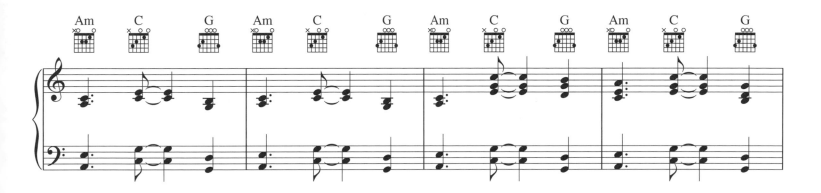

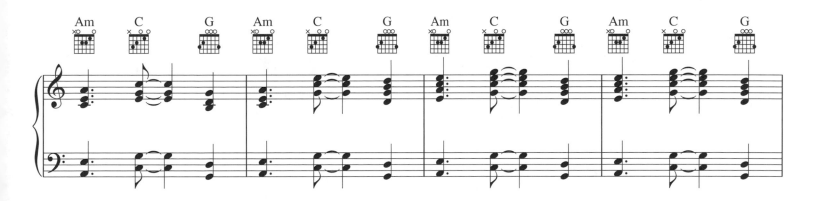

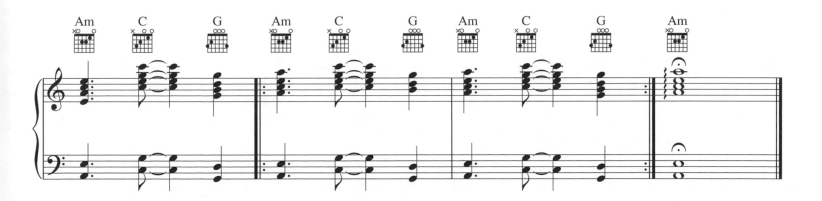

CARRY ON

Words and Music by
NORAH JONES

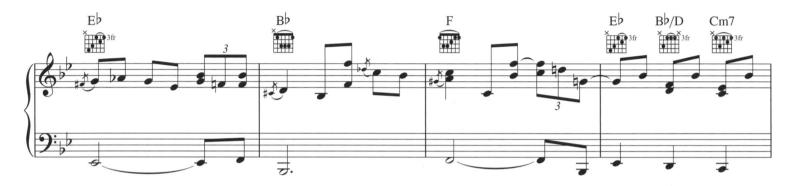

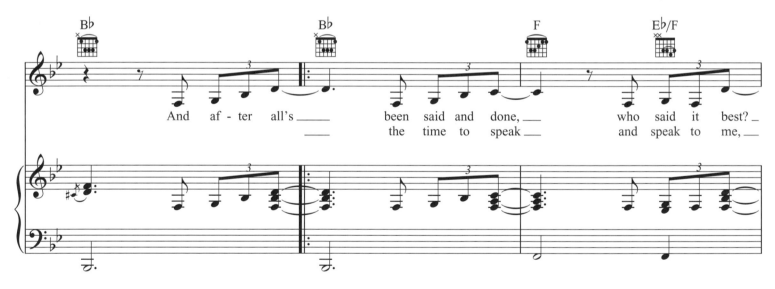

And af-ter all's _____ been said and done, ___ who said it best? _____
_____ the time to speak ___ and speak to me, ___

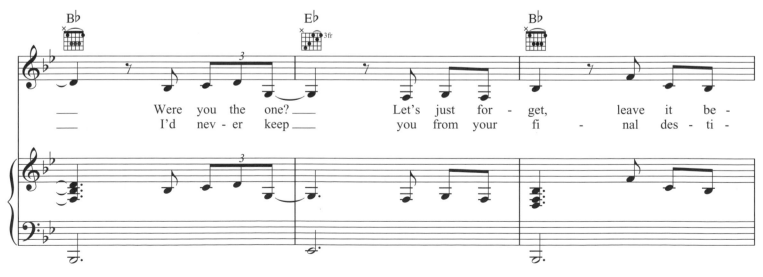

_____ Were you the one? _____ Let's just for - get, _____ leave it be -
_____ I'd nev - er keep ___ you from your fi - nal des - ti -

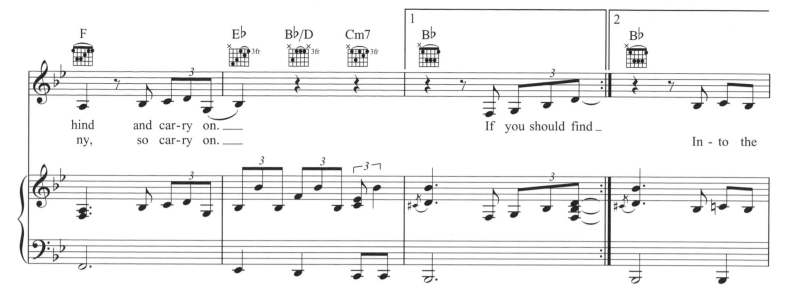

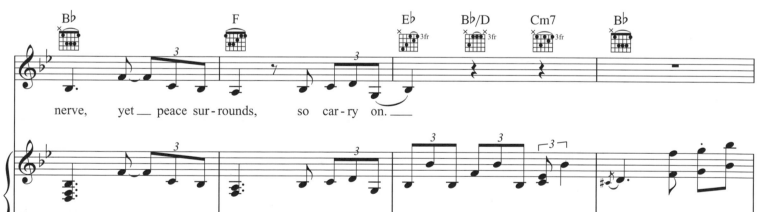

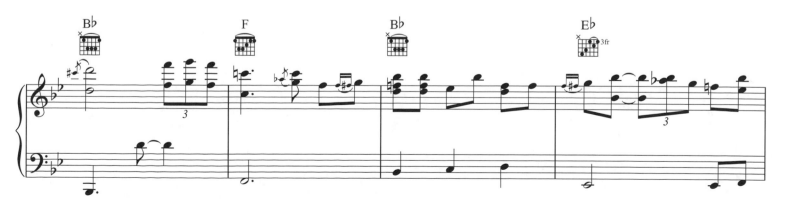

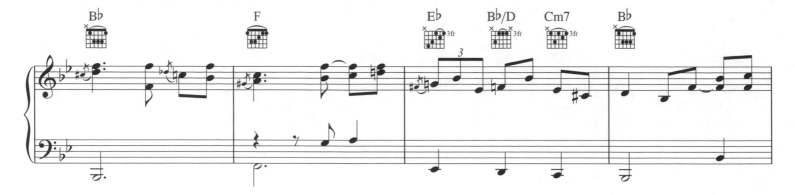

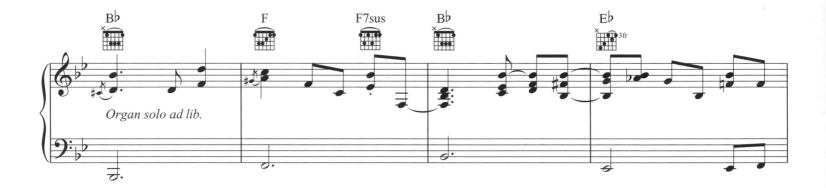

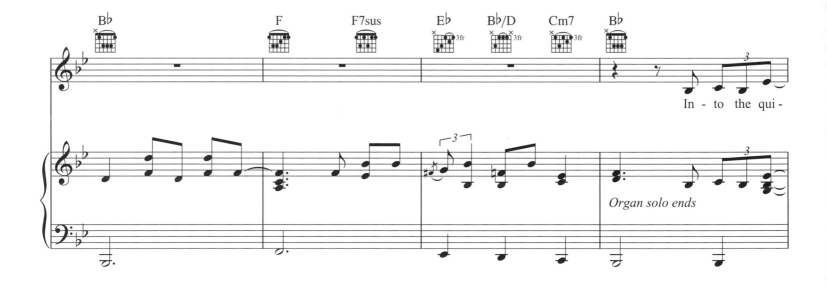

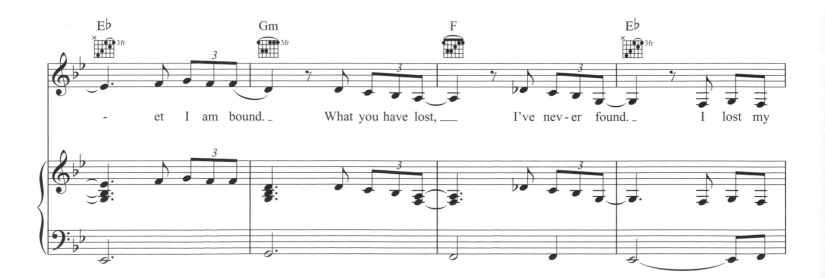

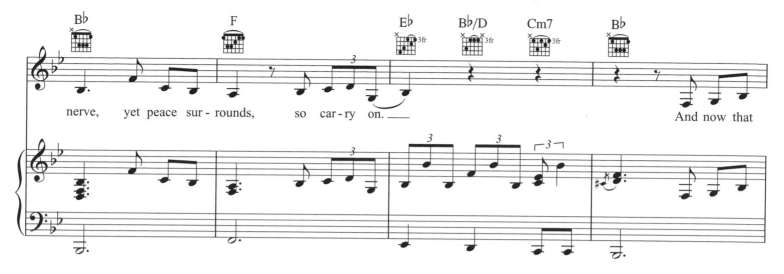

nerve, yet peace sur - rounds, so car - ry on. ___ And now that

all's been said and done, ___ who said it best? ___ Were you the one? ___ Let's just for -

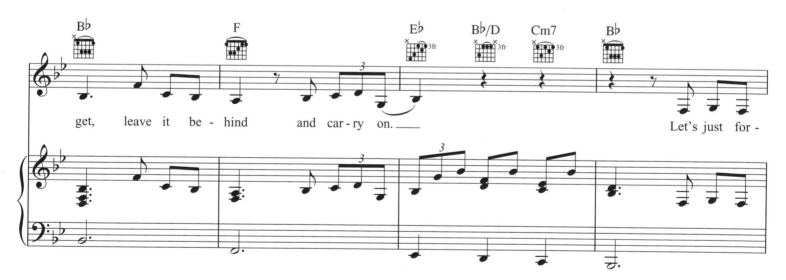

get, leave it be - hind and car - ry on. ___ Let's just for -

get, leave __ it be - hind and car - ry on. ___

AFRICAN FLOWER
(Petite Fleur Africaine)

By DUKE ELLINGTON

Moderate Afro-Cuban feel

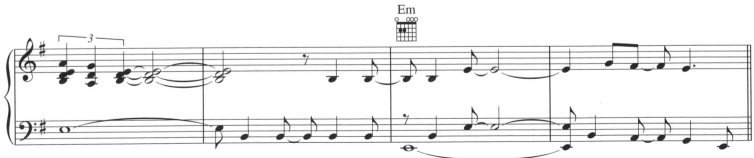

* Recorded a half step lower.

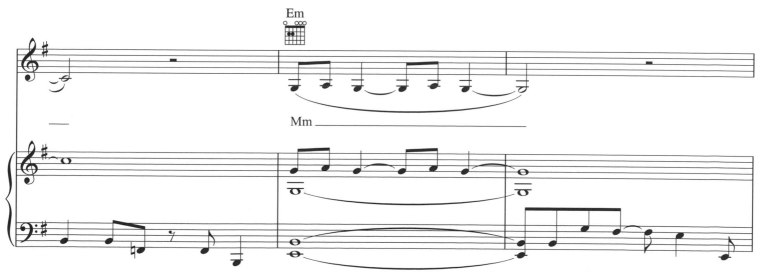

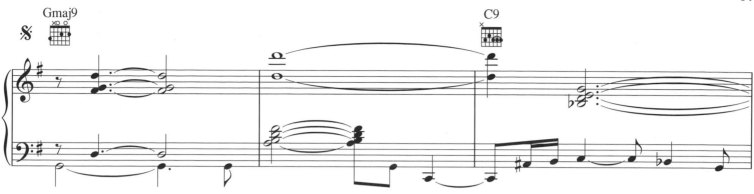

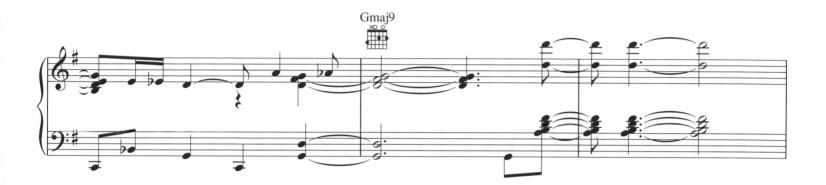

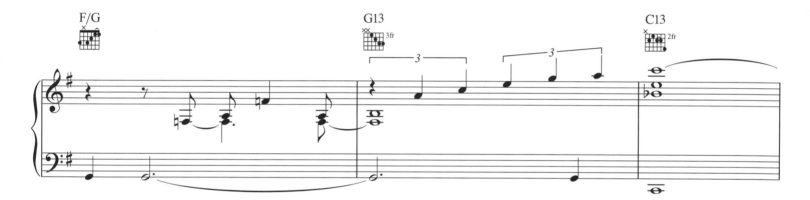

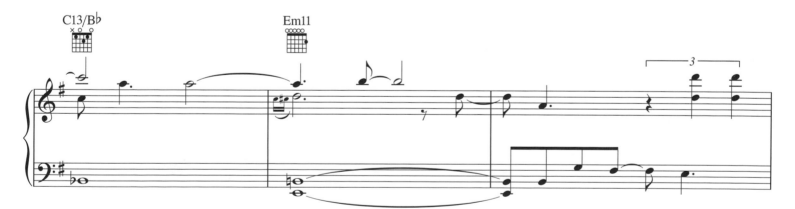

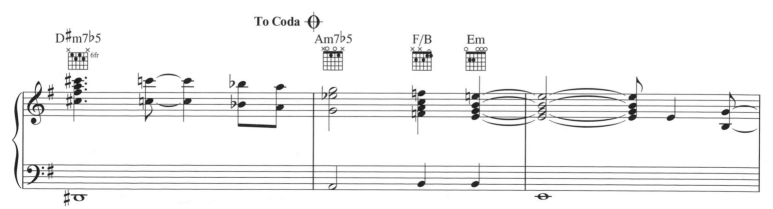

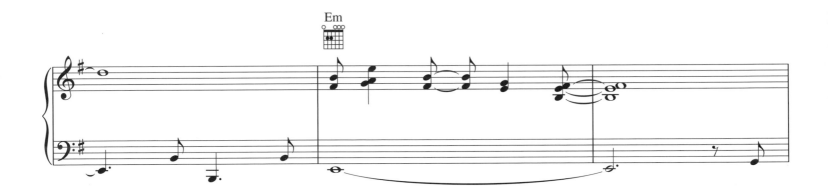

Ad lib. solo on repeats

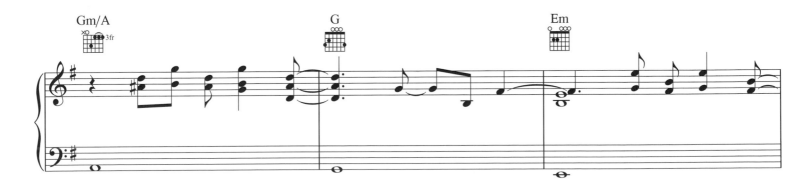

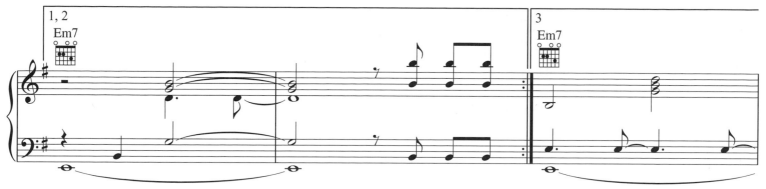

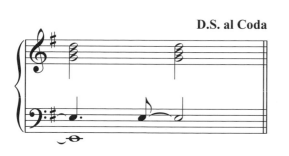

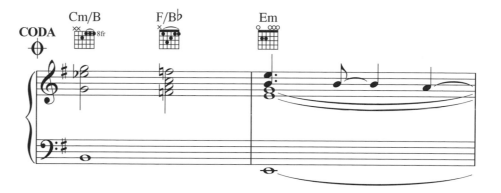

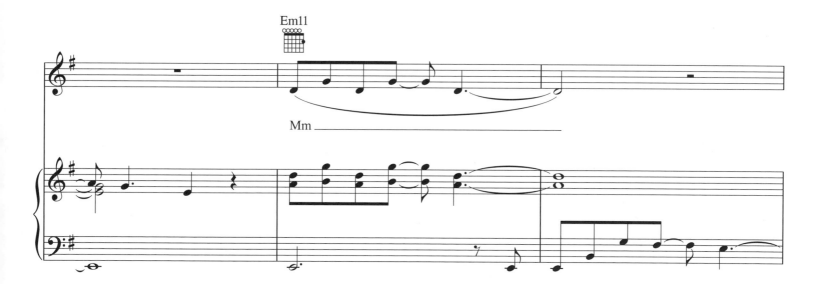

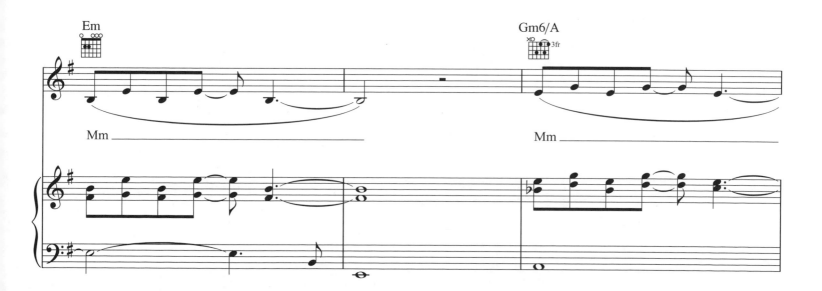

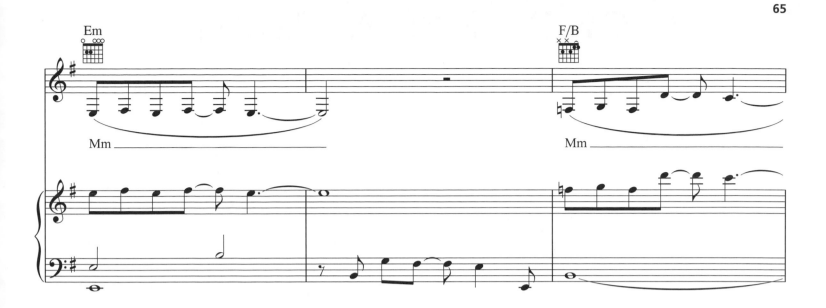

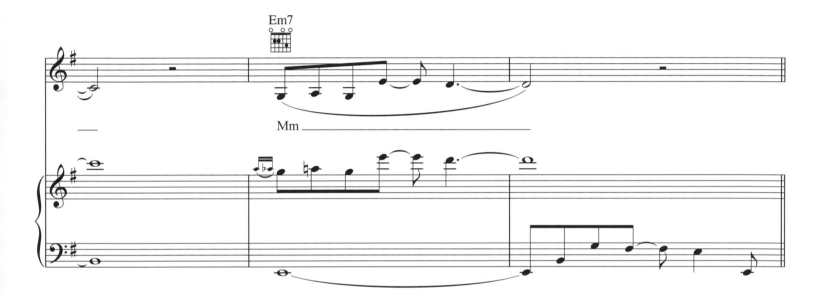

Play 3 times

Piano solo ad lib.

rit.

ONCE I HAD A LAUGH

Words and Music by
NORAH JONES

Once I had a laugh.___ And when I'm old-er, I will___
old - er but I will

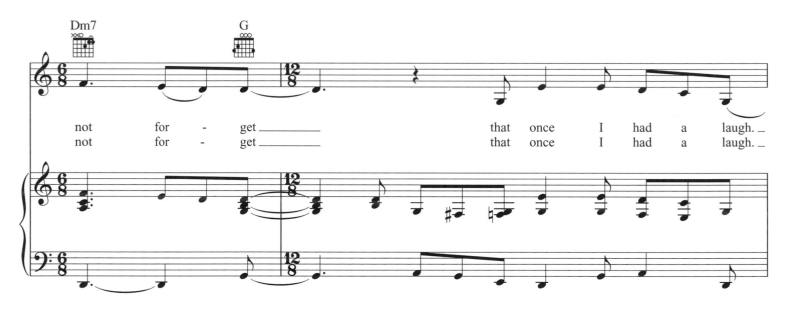

not for - get _____ that once I had a laugh.___
not for - get _____ that once I had a laugh.___

And when I'm tir - ed, I will___
And now I'm fall - ing but I will

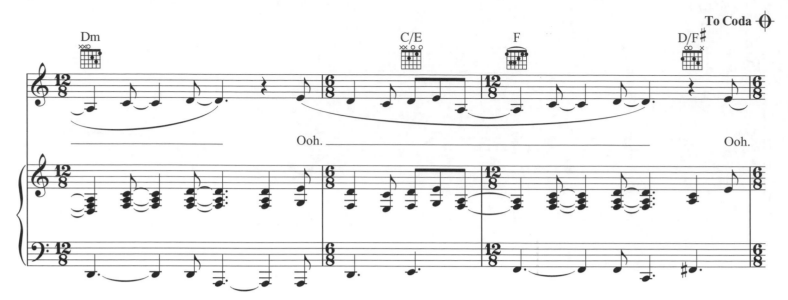

Ooh. _____ Ooh.

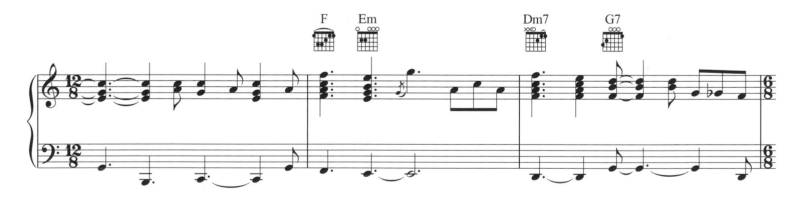

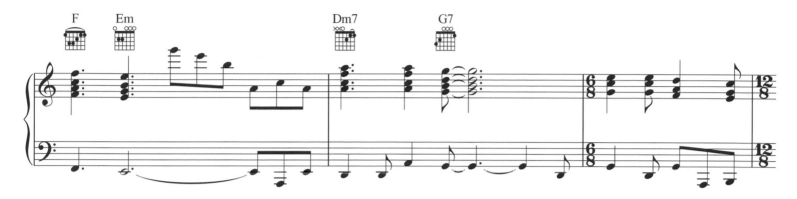

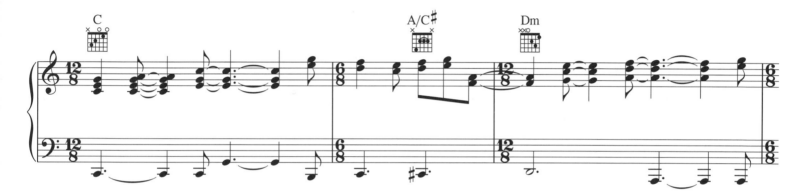

D.S. al Coda

Once I had a laugh _ and now I'm

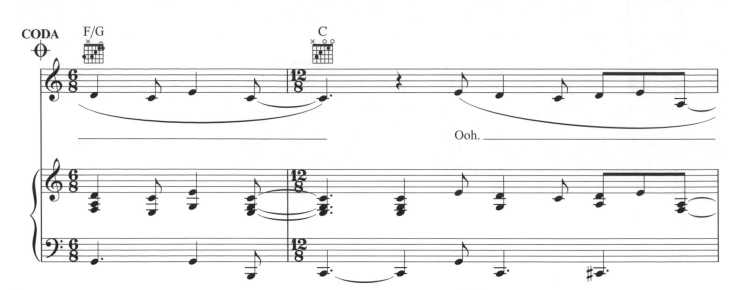

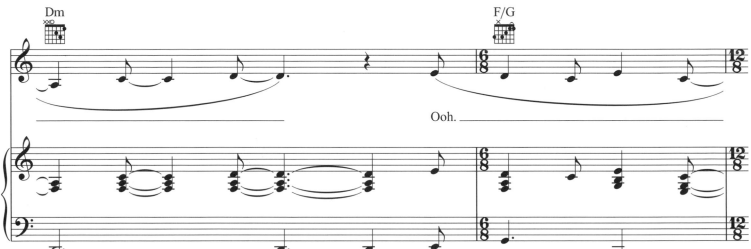

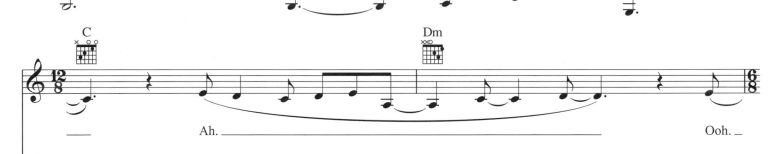

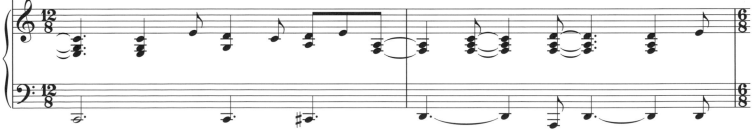

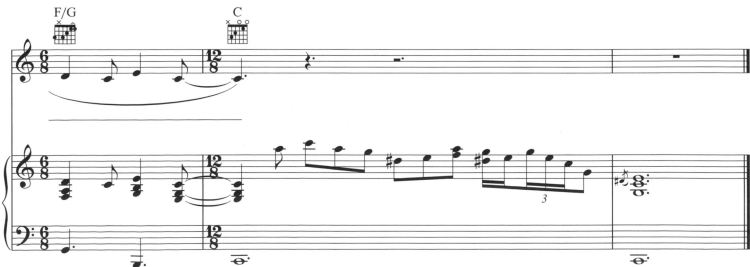